CW00421859

THE LATIN AMERICAN SONGBOOK

WISE PUBLICATIONS
LONDON/NEW YORK/PARIS/SYDNEY/COPENHAGEN/MADRID

EXCLUSIVE DISTRIBUTORS:
MUSIC SALES LIMITED
8/9 FRITH STREET,
LONDON W1V 5TZ, ENGLAND.
MUSIC SALES PTY LIMITED
120 ROTHSCHILD AVENUE,
ROSEBERY, NSW 2018,
AUSTRALIA.

ORDER NO. AM91981
ISBN 0-7119-4097-5
THIS BOOK © COPYRIGHT 1995 BY WISE PUBLICATIONS

COMPILED BY PETER EVANS AND PETER LAVENDER
BOOK DESIGN BY PEARCE MARCHBANK, STUDIO TWENTY
QUARKED BY BEN MAY

PRINTED IN THE UNITED KINGDOM BY
PAGE BROS., NORWICH, NORFOLK.

YOUR GUARANTEE OF QUALITY
AS PUBLISHERS, WE STRIVE TO PRODUCE EVERY BOOK TO THE
HIGHEST COMMERCIAL STANDARDS.
THIS BOOK HAS BEEN CAREFULLY DESIGNED TO MINIMISE AWKWARD PAGE
TURNS AND TO MAKE PLAYING FROM IT A REAL PLEASURE.
PARTICULAR CARE HAS BEEN GIVEN TO SPECIFYING ACID-FREE, NEUTRAL-
SIZED PAPER MADE FROM PULPS WHICH HAVE NOT BEEN ELEMENTAL
CHLORINE BLEACHED. THIS PULP IS FROM FARMED SUSTAINABLE FORESTS
AND WAS PRODUCED WITH SPECIAL REGARD FOR THE ENVIRONMENT.
THROUGHOUT, THE PRINTING AND BINDING HAVE BEEN PLANNED TO
ENSURE A STURDY, ATTRACTIVE PUBLICATION WHICH SHOULD GIVE YEARS
OF ENJOYMENT.
IF YOUR COPY FAILS TO MEET OUR HIGH STANDARDS, PLEASE INFORM US
AND WE WILL GLADLY REPLACE IT.

MUSIC SALES' COMPLETE CATALOGUE
DESCRIBES THOUSANDS OF TITLES AND IS AVAILABLE IN FULL COLOUR
SECTIONS BY SUBJECT, DIRECT FROM MUSIC SALES LIMITED.
PLEASE STATE YOUR AREAS OF INTEREST AND SEND A CHEQUE/POSTAL
ORDER FOR £1.50 FOR POSTAGE TO:
MUSIC SALES LIMITED, NEWMARKET ROAD,
BURY ST. EDMUNDS, SUFFOLK IP33 3YB.

ADIOS

ENGLISH WORDS BY EDDIE WOODS.
MUSIC & SPANISH WORDS BY ENRIC MADRIGUERA.

So, dear, this mes-sage to__ you I'm send-ing,__ A word of hope, from my__ ach-ing
por e-so mi al-ma tris-te se que - ja__ cuan-do a - si te can - ta__ su do -

heart
lor.

Smoothly

A - dios,_____ in leav-ing you, it grieves me to__ say a -
A - dios,_____ Me voy lin - da mo - re - na le - jos de

dios._____ I'll be so lone - ly, for you on - ly I
ti_____ El al - ma he - cha una pe - na por__ que al par -

PABLO THE DREAMER
(ADIOS MUCHACHOS)

MUSIC BY JULIO SANDERS. ENGLISH LYRIC BY ROBERTO LOPEZ.

A MAN AND A WOMAN
(UN HOMME ET UNE FEMME)

ORIGINAL WORDS BY PIERRE BAROUH. ENGLISH LYRIC BY JERRY KELLER. MUSIC BY FRANCIS LAI.

ALL MY LOVE (SOLO TU)

MUSIC BY F. MONTI ARDUINI. ENGLISH LYRIC BY PETER CALLANDER.

find you were no long-er mine.

All my love _____ thrown a-way af-ter all this time, _____

Last time Fade

_____ now there's no place for me in the fu-ture, you

see. I don't un-der-stand you I've done all I can

16

ARRIVEDERCI ROMA

WORDS BY GARINEI & GIOVANNINI. ENGLISH LYRIC BY CARL SIGMAN.
MUSIC BY RENATO RASCEL.

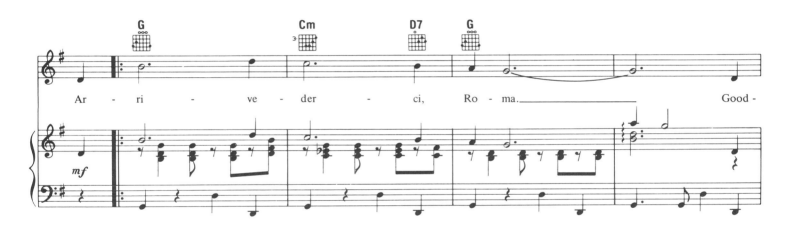

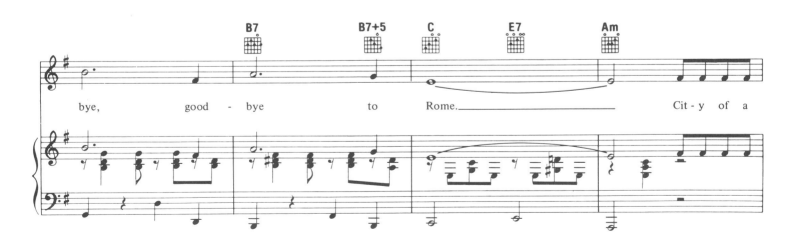

part._____ Save the wed-ding bells for my re-

turn - ing, Keep my lov-er's arms out-stretched and yearn - ing, Please be sure the

flame of love keeps burn-ing in {her his} heart._____ Ar -

heart._____

rit. e dim.

ALWAYS IN MY HEART

WORDS BY KIM GANNON. MUSIC BY ERNESTO LECUONA.

AMAPOLA

WORDS BY ALBERT GAMSE. MUSIC BY JOSEPH M. LACALLE.

A boy _____ found a dream up-on a
The boy _____ left his love up-on a

dis - tant shore _____ A maid _____
dis - tant shore _____ And sailed _____

with a way of whis-p'ring "si sen - or."   Each
from the one his arms were long - ing for.   He

night   while gui-tars would soft-ly play,
vowed   he'd re-turn one sun-ny day,

The tune seem'd to dance   'round the words that he'd
Once more to re-peat   what his heart had to

say: A - ma - po - la,   my pret-ty lit - tle
say:

CHORUS

pop - py _____ must co-py its en - dear - ing charm from

you. _____ A - ma - po - la, _____ A - ma -

po - la, _____ How I long to hear you say I

love_ you. A - ma - love you. _____

BRAZIL

MUSIC BY ARY BARROSO. ENGLISH LYRIC BY S.K. RUSSELL.

with still a mil - lion things to say,

Now

when twi - light dims the sky a - bove,

Re - call - ing thrills of our love,

BESAME MUCHO

ENGLISH WORDS BY SUNNY SKYLAR. MUSIC BY CONSUELO VELAZQUEZ.

leave me, _____
mu - cho, _____

Each lit - tle dream would take wing and my life would be
co - mo si fue - ra es - ta no - che la úl - ti - ma

through, _____
vez, _____

Bé - - - - - - sa - me
Bé - - - - - - sa - me

mu - cho, _____
mu - cho, _____

Love me for - ev - er and make all my dreams come
que ten - go mie - do per - der - te, per - der - te des -

1.

true. _____
pués. _____

2.

true. _____
pués. _____

poco rit.

R.H.

CIELITO LINDO

TRADITIONAL.

ay ay ay! _____ Can - - - ta y no

llo - res, _____ Por - que can - tan - do se a - le - gran Cie -

- li - to Lin - do los ___ co - ra - zo - nes. _____

zo - nes. _____

CUANTO LE GUSTA

WORDS BY RAY GILBERT. MUSIC BY GABRIEL RUIZ.

where we go - in'? And what- a we gon - na do? We're on our way to

"some- where", the three of us and you. What- 'll we see there,

who will be there, What- 'll be the big sur - prise? There may be se - no -
(ca - bal -

ri - tas with dark and flash - ing eyes, We're on our way,
le - ros) (I'll take a train,)

FEELINGS (DIME)

BY MORRIS ALBERT & LOUIS GASTE.

SLIGHTLY OUT OF TUNE (DESAFINADO)

ENGLISH LYRIC BY JON HENDRICKS & JESSIE CAVANAUGH. MUSIC BY ANTONIO CARLOS JOBIM.

ESO BESO

WORDS & MUSIC BY JOE & NOEL SHERMAN.

it's got a lot!_____ When we sam - ba is the swing - in' - est

way to make a - mor! As we dip and sway, And we ca -

ress this way, The sam - ba seems to say: Love is here to

stay, Like the sam - ba sound, My heart be - gins to pound, I go

FLY ME TO THE MOON (IN OTHER WORDS)

WORDS & MUSIC BY BART HOWARD.

GREEN EYES

WORDS BY L. WOLFE GILBERT & REG CONNELLY. MUSIC BY NILO MENENDEZ.

GUANTANAMERA

WORDS BY JOSE MARTI. MUSIC ADAPTATION BY HECTOR ANGULO AND PETE SEEGER.

Spanish verses

1. *Yo soy un hombre sincero,*
   De donde crece la palma,
   Y antes de morirme quiero,
   Echar mis versos del alma.

2. *Mi verso es de un verde claro,*
   Y de un carmin encendido,
   Mi verso es un cierro herido,
   Que busca en el monte amparo.

3. *Con los pobres de la tierra,*
   Quiero yo mi suerte echar,
   El arroyo de la sierra,
   Me complace mas que el mar.

NOTE - Repeat chorus after
each of the above verses.

Literal translation

Guantanamera: A lady
of Guantanamo
Guajira: Young woman

I'm a sincere man from
the land of palms. Before
dying, I wish to pour forth
the poems of my soul.

My verses are soft green but
also a flaming red. My
verses are like wounded
fauns seeking refuge in the
forest.

I want to share my fate with
the world's humble. A little
mountain stream pleases me
more than the ocean.

English lyrics

1. I'm just a man who is trying -
   to do some good before dying,
   To ask each man and his brother -
   To bear no ill toward each other.
   This life will never be hollow -
   To those who listen and follow.

2. I write my rhymes with no learning,
   And yet with truth they are burning,
   But is the world waiting for them?
   Or will they all just ignore them?
   Have I a poet's illusion,
   A dream to die in seclusion? (Chorus)

3. A little brook on a mountain,
   The cooling spray of a fountain -
   Arouse in me an emotion, more
   than the vast boundless ocean,
   For there's a wealth beyond measure
   In little things that we treasure.
   (final Chorus, in Spanish)

GRANADA

MUSIC BY AGUSTIN LARA. ENGLISH LYRIC BY DOROTHY DODD.

mem - ber   the   splen - dor   that   once   was   Gra -
blush   of   the   snow - clad   Si - er - ra   Ne -

C6

To Coda ⊕

na - da. _____
va - da. _____   It

C

still   can   be   found   in   the   hills   all   a - round   as   I

Em

wan - der a - long, _____

66

HISTORY OF LOVE
(HISTORIA DE UN AMOR)

ENGLISH LYRIC BY DOROTHY DODD. MUSIC BY CARLOS ALMARAN.

Moderately

If you want to learn the his-tor-y of love,_____ First you have to solve the mys-t'ry that is love,_____

—— It's en-chant-ment, it's temp-ta-tion, And the kind of fasc-in-a-tion that is mine when I'm with

you._____ Love's a stor-y that be-gins but nev-er ends._____ And if on-ly we were

slight-ly clos-er friends,_____ We could stud-y it to-geth-er, And per-haps dis-co-ver

wheth-er all it says is real-ly true. Love's a feel-ing that we don't ev-er quite un-der-

stand, Till we hear a cer-tain voice, Feel the touch of a hand, Then the mag-ic of the

ag - es_____ will be there for us to see,_____ Ev- 'ry time we turn the

HOW INSENSITIVE

MUSIC BY ANTONIO CARLOS JOBIM. ORIGINAL LYRICS BY VINICIUS DE MORAES.
ENGLISH LYRICS BY NORMAN GIMBEL.

LA BAMBA

ADAPTED & ARRANGED BY RITCHIE VALENS.

LOVE ME WITH ALL YOUR HEART (CUANDO CALIENTA EL SOL)

MUSIC BY CARLOS RIGUAL & CARLOS A. MARTINOLI. ORIGINAL WORDS BY MARIO RIGUAL.
ENGLISH LYRIC BY MICHAEL VAUGHN.

Moderately slow with a strong beat

Love me with all your heart, that's all I want, love;

Love me with all of your heart, or not at all;

Just pro-mise me this: _____ that you'll give me _ all your kiss-es, _ Ev-'ry

win-ter, _ ev-'ry sum-mer, _ ev-'ry fall.

When we are far a-part _ or when you're near me, _

Love me with all of your heart as I love you;

LITTLE BOAT (O BARQUINHO)

MUSIC BY ROBERTO MENESCAL. ORIGINAL WORDS BY RONALDO BOSCOLI.
ENGLISH LYRIC BY BUDDY KAYE.

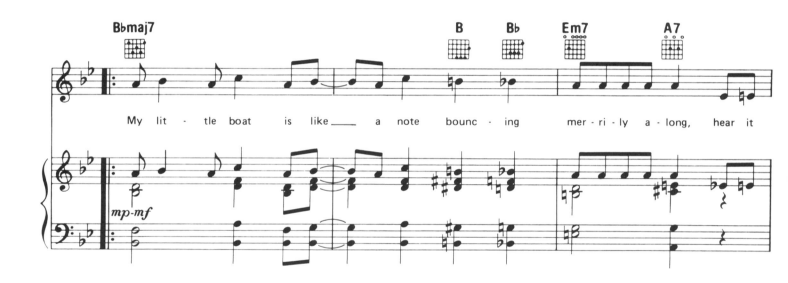

My lit-tle boat is like a note bounc-ing mer-ri-ly a-long, hear it

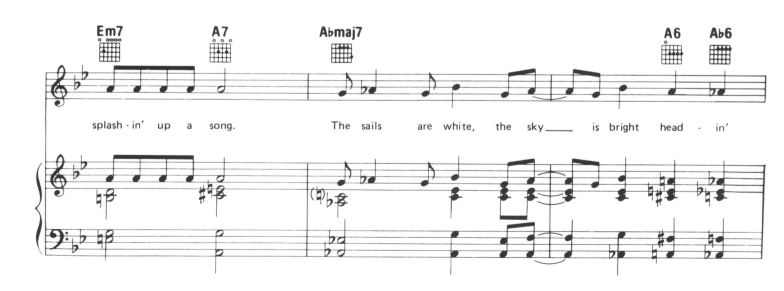

splash-in' up a song. The sails are white, the sky is bright head-in'

MAGIC IS THE MOONLIGHT

MUSIC BY MARIA GREVER. ENGLISH WORDS BY CHARLES PASQUALE.

MEDITATION (MEDITACAO)

ORIGINAL WORDS BY NEWTON MENDONCA. ENGLISH LYRIC BY NORMAN GIMBEL.
MUSIC BY ANTONIO CARLOS JOBIM.

MALAGUENA

ENGLISH WORDS BY GEORGE BROWN. MUSIC BY ERNESTO LECUONA.

me That must burn, die out, so I can be free,

If no spark ling-ers with - in when the storm is past, I'll be yours, I'll be

yours, yours at last.————   past, I'll be yours, I'll be

yours, yours at last.————

NON DIMENTICAR

MUSIC BY P.G. REDI. ENGLISH LYRIC BY SHELLEY DOBBINS.
ORIGINAL ITALIAN LYRIC BY MICHELE GALDIERI.

ONE NOTE SAMBA
(SAMBA DE UMA NOTA SO)

ORIGINAL WORDS BY N. MENDONCA. ENGLISH LYRIC BY JON HENDRICKS.
MUSIC BY ANTONIO CARLOS JOBIM.

PERDIDO

MUSIC BY JUAN TIZOL. WORDS BY HARRY LENK AND ERVIN DRAKE.

le - ro, ____ I swayed as ____ they played a ____ bo - le - ro, ____ I kissed 'neath ____ a list - ing ____ som - bre - ro ____ And that's when my heart de - part - ed. ____ High was the sun when I held ____ {her} {him} close, ____

QUIET NIGHTS OF QUIET STARS
(CORCOVADO)

ENGLISH WORDS BY GENE LEES. MUSIC & ORIGINAL WORDS BY ANTONIO CARLOS JOBIM.

SONG OF THE JET (SAMBA DO AVIAO)

ORIGINAL WORDS & MUSIC BY ANTONIO CARLOS JOBIM. ENGLISH WORDS BY GENE LEES.

SO NICE

MUSIC & ORIGINAL LYRICS BY MARCOS VALLE & PAULO SERGIO VALLE.
ENGLISH LYRICS BY NORMAN GIMBEL.

then give his heart to me. Some-one who's read-y to give love a start with me.

Oh yes, that would be so nice.

Should it be you and me, I could see it would be

nice.

nice.

SWEET AND GENTLE (ME LO DIJO ADELA)

ENGLISH WORDS BY GEORGE THORN. MUSIC BY OTILIO PORTAL.

quiet! And then one mag-ic night I learned to do the cha-cha,

And now I'll nev-er be the same, For I have turned in-to a danc-ing cu-ca-

ra-cha! And my mu-cha-cha is to blame,

How can I be gen-tle, Sweet and sen-ti-

men- tal,   While the cha-cha's play- ing,

And my heart is sway- ing, I find   that   I am ev- en danc- ing when I'm

walk- ing,   I'm haunt- ed by that cha- cha beat,   I hear   the

rhy- thm start when- ev - er we are talk- ing,   I do the cha- cha in my

THE COFFEE SONG

WORDS & MUSIC BY BOB HILLIARD & DICK MILES.

They've got an aw - ful lot of cof - fee in Bra - zil. _____
Why they could per - co - late the o - cean in Bra - zil. _____

You can't get cher - ry so - da 'cause they've got to sell their
And when their ham and eggs need sa - vor, cof - fee ketch - up

quo - ta, and the way things are I guess they nev - er will. _____
gives them fla - vor, cof - fee pick - les way out sell the dill. _____

They've got a zil - lion tons of cof - fee in Bra - zil. _____
Why they put cof - fee in the cof - fee in Bra - zil. _____

RECADO BOSSA NOVA (THE GIFT)

WORDS & MUSIC BY DJALMA FERREIRA & LUIZ ANTONIO.

VAYA CON DIOS

WORDS & MUSIC BY LARRY RUSSELL, INEZ JAMES & BUDDY PEPPER.

Moderate Waltz Tempo

THE GIRL FROM IPANEMA
(GAROTA DE IPANEMA)

ORIGINAL WORDS BY VINICIUS DE MORAES. ENGLISH LYRIC BY NORMAN GIMBEL.
MUSIC BY ANTONIO CARLOS JOBIM.